GLORIA Children's Books

Nihil Obstat, Arthur J. Scanlan, S.T.D., Censor Liborum
Imprimatur ✠ Francis Cardinal Spellman,
Archbishop of New York
Cum Permissu Superiorum

William J. Hirten Co., Cumberland, RI

The Holy Family

Jesus and His Parents

by Daniel A. Lord, S.J.

The Story of the Holy Family

Once upon a time, there lived the
loveliest family the world had ever seen.
The head of the family was Joseph.
He was a carpenter.
The Mother's name was Mary.
She was sweet
and dear and good and beautiful.
Her Son's name was Jesus.
He was the most beautiful
Child in the world.
He was the greatest person that ever lived.
He was the Son of God, made man.

5

They lived in a little house in a small town call Nazareth.
It was a poor little house, but Mary kept it clean and charming.
Near it was the carpenter shop where Joseph worked. He did not make a great deal of money. But he was honest and hard-working.
And the things he made with his tools made the people in the village very happy.
Jesus was an obedient, loving boy.
Everyone thought He was smart and nice.
He loved His Mother and Joseph, His foster father, so much that He did all He could to make them happy.

Though He was only a boy, Jesus was the
most important person in this family.
For His real Father was God.
And He was King of Kings,
the greatest person in the world.
Yet He knew how boys and girls
are supposed to behave.
They are to obey their parents.
They are to love them and make them happy.
So Jesus did just this.
He helped His Mother around the House.
He went to the village well to get
water for the family.
He ran errands for her and always smiled
when she asked Him to do her a favor.
"Yes, indeed, Mother," He said,
and hurried off to do what she wished.

Joseph and Mary loved each
other very much.
Joseph never spoke roughly
or loudly to his wife.
He thanked her for whatever
she did for him.
He loved her meals.
He was pleased with the way
she kept house.
And Mary was happy that she could make
the house beautiful for Joseph and Jesus.
So they lived in peace and joy.
There were no arguments.
Love was all around them.
No wonder they were happy.

Let's visit this Holy Family together.
As we come near,
we can hear the sound of Joseph's hammer.
He is busy in his little shop.
There he stands at his work table
making a nice, sturdy chair for an old lady.
There on the wall is a crutch
he made for a little boy who was hurt.
And He has just finished a table
for a newly married couple.

13

We walk into the kitchen.
There is Mary busy around the house.
She has swept the floor until it is spotless.
Near the wall is a basket of clean clothes
she has just washed.
Now she starts to cook dinner
for Joseph and Jesus.
It is a plain, simple meal.
She cannot spend
much money on food.
But it smells very good,
because it is flavored with love.

15

It is dinner time.
Joseph and Jesus sit down at the table.
Mary is still busy getting the food ready.
She brings it over to the table
in a deep, hot bowl.
It smells so good, but is just the
plain food of poor people.
They cannot buy things
that are fine or expensive.
Joseph says grace.
He asks God to bless them
and to bless what they will eat.
Then Mary serves the food
and they all eat.

All the time the Holy Family
talks to each other.
How cheerful it sounds!
Jesus tells about the games He played.
He tells about His friends.
He always speaks kindly of them.
Joseph and Mary talk to each other
about the events of the day.
When Joseph tells a little joke,
they all laugh together.
When Mary tells about something
sad in one of the near-by houses,
they are all sad.
But mostly they are very happy.
Because they love one another so much
there is always happiness all around them.

19

It is the morning of the Sabbath.
Always when they wake-up,
Jesus, Mary, and Joseph
say their morning prayers.
They ask God, the Heavenly Father,
to bless the whole day.
They offer to Him everything they will do.
They say, "Dear Father, be with us all day,
and help us with all we do."
But this is a Holy Day.
So they all go to their parish church.
This is called a synagogue.
They go very happily, for they know
this is the House of God.

They smile at their friends along the way.
They wish them a cheerful Good Morning.
For they love all their neighbors
and wish them well.
Their little church is very poor.
But it is very important.
Here they will talk to God and
God will talk to them.
They enter quietly.
They bow their heads to
honor God the Father.
They pray with their hearts.
Then they pray aloud with all
the people around them.
They feel very close to their Heavenly Father.
They know that their Heavenly Father
is always close to them.

Jesus is well liked by all His friends.
They are glad when He comes out
to play with them.
Mary is friendly with all the women.
They know how sweet she is.
She never speaks unkindly of anyone.
When they need help,
she always gives it gladly.
Joseph has many friends too.
They have a deep trust in him.
He is honest and willing to help.
They can call him any time they need help,
and he comes immediately.

When there is a family party,
the three of them always go.
When one of their relatives has a birthday,
they help to celebrate it.
They are always invited
to the wedding celebrations.
They like to see their friends happy.
They enjoy eating with their relatives.
They like to join in the songs that everyone sings.
They love to hear their friends
laughing and singing.
But on evenings when they are at home together,
they are just as happy.
They love to talk quietly.
They are satisfied just to be together.
Theirs is a happy home. And when they
enter anyone's home, they make it happy too.